To ....

You are hereby invited to a philosophical garden party at 3 Clover Close on Saturday June 23rd (Midsummer Eve) at 7pm. During the evening we shall hopefully solve the mystery of life. Please bring warm sweaters and bright ideas suitable for solving the riddles of philosophy.

Joanna Ingebrigtsen & Sophie Amundsen

This edition first published in 1999 by The Orion Publishing Group

Developed under licence from Aschehoug & Co, Oslo, and based on the novel
Sophie's World by Jostein Gaarder, with the kind permission of the author.
Portions of text © The Sophie's World Consortium

Book designed by Lorraine Brown at Redback Design Ltd, Cambridge
Picture research by Charlotte Lorimer and Robert Hyde

UK ISBN 075281 867 8
Developed by Galileo Multimedia Ltd

Printed in Italy by Printer Trento Srl

The Sophie Foundation

The Sophie Foundation was established in Norway in 1997 by the author of
Sophie's World, Jostein Gaarder, and his wife, Siri Dannevig.

The purpose of The Sophie Foundation is to award an annual international
environmental prize of US $ 100,000. The Sophie Prize will be awarded to an individual
or organisation that, in a pioneering or a particularly creative way, has pointed to
alternatives to current development and put such alternatives into practice.

If you would like to learn more about The Sophie Prize, please contact:

The Sophie Foundation

Nedre gate 8, N-0551, Oslo, Norway
Phone: + 47 22 87 01 00 Fax: + 47 22 87 00 99 E-mail: sophiefo@online.no

SOPHIE'S WORLD

JOURNAL
&
BOOK OF DAYS

The Orion Publishing Group
London

JANUARY

1 _____

2 _____

3 _____

4 _____

5 _____

6 _____

7 _____

8 _____

9 _____

JANUARY

10

11

12

13

14

15

16

"Personally I think philosophy is a more important subject than English grammar. It would be therefore be a sensible priority of values to have philosophy on the timetable and cut down a bit on English lessons."

Sophie

DEMOCRITUS (C. 460 BC-370 BC)

Democritus was the last of the great natural philosophers. Very little is known about his life but we do know he was from the small town of Abdera on the northern Aegean coast.

Democritus believed that nature consisted of an unlimited number and variety of atoms. Some were round and smooth, others were irregular and jagged. And precisely because they were so different they could join together into all kinds of different bodies. But, however infinite they might be in number and shape, they were all eternal, immutable and indivisible.

When a body - a tree or an animal, for instance - died and disintegrated, the atoms dispersed and could be used again in new bodies. Atoms moved around in space, but because they had "hooks" and "barbs", they could join together to form all the things we see around us.

Democritus' solution to the problem of change was that no single atom - the basic units from which everything was made - actually changed at all. Instead he concluded that the only thing that actually did change was the arrangement of atoms.

But what about the "soul"? Surely that could not consist of atoms, of material things? Indeed it could. Democritus believed that the soul was made up of special round, smooth "soul atoms." When a human being died, the soul atoms flew in all directions, and could then become part of a new soul formation.

This meant that human beings had no immortal soul, another belief that many people share today. They believe, like Democritus, that "soul" is connected with brain, and that we cannot have any form of consciousness once the brain disintegrates.

"BY CONVENTION THERE IS COLOUR, BY CONVENTION SWEETNESS, BY CONVENTION BITTERNESS, BUT IN REALITY THERE ARE ONLY ATOMS AND SPACE"

DEMOCRITUS

J ANUARY

17

18

19

20

21

22

23

"IN TRUTH WE
KNOW NOTHING,
FOR TRUTH LIES
IN THE DEPTH"

DEMOCRITUS

JANUARY

24 _____

25 _____

26 _____

27 _____

28 _____

29 _____

30 _____

31 _____

"IGNORANCE IS THE ONLY EVIL"

SOCRATES

SOCRATES (470 BC-399 BC)

Socrates is possibly the most enigmatic figure in the entire history of philosophy. He never wrote a single line. Yet he is one of the philosophers who has had the greatest influence on European thought, not least because of the dramatic nature of his death.

Socrates thought that a philosopher is someone who recognises that there is a lot he does not understand, and is troubled by it. In that sense, he is still wiser than all those who brag about their knowledge of things they really know nothing about. Socrates himself said, "One thing only I know and that is that I know nothing."

But while he constantly questioned the extent of his own knowledge (a method that Descartes was to employ some 2000 years later), Socrates believed that it is possible for man to obtain absolute truths about the Universe. He felt that it was necessary to establish a solid foundation for our knowledge, a foundation which he believed lay in man's reason. With his unshakeable faith in human reason Socrates was decidedly a rationalist.

In the year 399 BC Socrates was accused of "introducing new gods" (the "divine inner voices" he claimed to hear in his head) and corrupting youth, as well as not believing in the accepted gods. Although the government of Athens was one of the world's earliest democracies, Socrates, on the other hand, let everyone know he believed it was better for the state to be ruled by a single person, whom he described as "the one who knows." Some regarded Socrates' outspoken views as a threat to the very fabric of Athenian life. Worried by his anti-democratic influence over the many young aristocrats (including Plato) involved in this Socratic think-tank, a jury of 501 found him guilty by a slender majority.

> "ONE OUGHT NOT TO RETURN A WRONG NOR AN INJURY TO ANY PERSON, HOWEVER STRONG THE PROVOCATION"
>
> SOCRATES

JOURNAL

"I AM NOT AN ATHENIAN OR A GREEK,
BUT A CITIZEN OF THE WORLD"

SOCRATES

FEBRUARY

1

2

3

4

5

6

7

PLATO (c. 427-347 BC)

Plato was 29 when Socrates died, but it is not known when he started to write his many dialogues (most of which we still have) featuring Socrates as their central figure.

Socrates had a profound effect upon Plato whose own ideas only become clearly distinguishable from Socratic thought in his later works.

He may have been in his fifties when he co-founded his school with the mathematician Theaetetus. The school was named the Academy after the legendary Greek hero Academus. Through the Academy Plato hoped to provide a good education for the future rulers of Athens and other city-states. The subjects taught were philosophy, astronomy, gymnastics, mathematics and especially geometry. The inscription over the door of the Academy read "let no one ignorant of geometry enter here." Amongst his pupils was Aristotle who, like Plato, was to be one of the most influential philosophers who ever lived.

"PHILOSOPHY BEGINS IN WONDER"

PLATO

Plato believed that everything tangible in nature "flows." So there are no "substances" that do not dissolve. Absolutely everything that belongs to the "material world" is made of a material that time can erode, but everything is made after a timeless "mold" or "form" that is eternal and immutable.

Why are horses the same? There is something that all horses have in common, something that enables us to identify them as horses. A particular horse "flows," naturally. It might be old and lame, and in time it will die. But the "form" of the horse is eternal and immutable.

That which is eternal and immutable, to Plato, is therefore not a physical "basic substance," as it was for Empedocles and Democritus. Plato's conception was of eternal and immutable patterns, spiritual and abstract in their nature, that all things are fashioned after.

FEBRUARY

ARE WOMEN AND MEN EQUALLY SENSIBLE?

She was not so sure
about that. It was what
Plato meant by sensible.
Sophie was sure that he
would also have said
women had the same
common sense as men.

SOPHIE

8

9

10

11

12

13

14

"THE DIRECTION IN WHICH
EDUCATION STARTS A MAN WILL
DETERMINE HIS FUTURE LIFE"

PLATO

FEBRUARY

15

16

17

18

19

20

21

I t was almost as if she had herself emerged from an underground cave. Sophie felt she saw nature in a completely different way after reading about Plato.

SOPHIE

ARISTOTLE (384-322 BC)

Aristotle entered Plato's Academy as a 17 year-old student. He excelled and soon became a teacher. He remained at the Academy until Plato's death, some twenty years later.

Unlike Plato, Aristotle was preoccupied with "the natural processes." While Plato used his reason, Aristotle used his senses as well: he got down on all fours and studied frogs and fish, anemones and poppies.

The significance of Aristotle in European culture is due not least to the fact that he created the terminology that scientists use today. He was the great organiser who founded and classified the various sciences.

Aristotle thought that things that are in the human soul were purely reflections of natural objects. So nature was the real world.

Why does it rain? You have probably learned that it rains because the moisture in the clouds cools and condenses into raindrops that are drawn to the earth by the force of gravity. Aristotle would have agreed. But he would have added that so far you have only mentioned three of the causes. The "material cause" is that the moisture (the clouds) was there at the precise moment when the air cooled. The "efficient cause" is that the moisture cools, and the "formal cause" is that the "form," or nature of the water, is to fall to the earth. But if you stopped there, Aristotle would add that it rains because plants and animals need rain-water in order to grow. This he called the "final cause." Aristotle assigns the raindrops a life-task, or "purpose."

That is not the nature of scientific reasoning today. We say that although food and water are necessary conditions of life for man, it is not the purpose of water or oranges to be food for us. But Aristotle believed that there is a purpose behind everything in nature. It rains so that plants can grow; oranges and grapes grow so that people can eat them.

"I HAVE GAINED THIS BY
PHILOSOPHY: THAT I DO
WITHOUT BEING COMMANDED
WHAT OTHERS DO ONLY FROM
FEAR OF THE LAW"

ARISTOTLE

FEBRUARY

22

23

24

25

26

27

28

29 leap year

ACTUALLY,
DARKNESS HAS NO
EXISTENCE OF ITS OWN.
It's only a lack of light.

SOPHIE

"ALL MEN BY NATURE DESIRE TO KNOW"

ARISTOTLE

"ONE SWALLOW DOES NOT MAKE A SUMMER"

ARISTOTLE

JOURNAL

MARCH

1 _____

2 _____

3 _____

4 _____

5 _____

6 _____

7 _____

"Y ou've been gone for five hours"... Joanna said sharply. Sophie shook her head. "No, I've been gone for more than a *thousand years.*"

SOPHIE

AUGUSTINE (354-430)

Augustine lived from 354 to 430. In this one person's life we can observe the transition from late antiquity to the early Middle Ages.

He was not a Christian all his life. Augustine examined several different religions and philosophies before becoming a Christian in his later years.

He was completely preoccupied with what we like to call the "problem of evil." For a time he was influenced by the Stoics, who held that there was no sharp division between good and evil. However, his principal leanings were toward the other significant philosophy of late antiquity, Neoplatonism. In this philosophy he came across the idea that all existence is divine in nature. Augustine believed, like Plotinus, that evil is the absence of God. He maintained that evil comes from mankind's disobedience - in his own words, "the good will is God's work; the evil will is the falling away from God's work."

The Christianity of St. Augustine is largely influenced by Platonic ideas. You could say that it was St. Augustine who "christianised" Plato, helping Greek philosophy to be carried over to the new age via the Church.

"LORD, MAKE ME CHASTE, BUT NOT YET"

AUGUSTINE

St. Augustine's theology is considerably removed from the humanism of Athens. But he wasn't dividing humanity into two groups - those who would be saved and those who would not. He was merely expounding the Biblical doctrine of salvation and damnation. Augustine explained this in a learned work called *The City of God*, in which he put forward the view that there is no salvation outside the Church.

Not until the Reformation in the sixteenth century was there any protest against this idea.

"WE MAKE A
LADDER OF OUR
VICES, IF WE
TRAMPLE THOSE
SAME VICES
UNDERFOOT"

AUGUSTINE

MARCH

8

9

10

11

12

13

14

15

March

16 _____

17 _____

18 _____

19 _____

20 _____

21 _____

"Ssh"

Alberto held up one hand as priests do when they want the congregation to be seated. _"The Middle Ages began at four"_ he said

ALBERTO

"KNOWLEDGE IS POWER"

Francis Bacon

Sir Francis Bacon (1561-1626)

Bacon was a man of many parts, the principal ones being politics, law, philosophy and science. He became a Member of Parliament at the age of 23 and eventually rose to the post of Lord Chancellor.

It was science that fascinated him the most, and he was truly one of the first visionaries to understand that science would give mankind the kind of power over nature that had never previously been imagined. Indeed Newton and Darwin, who followed him, both acknowledged their debt to Bacon.

His real place in the history of philosophy was the pursuit of a new way of expressing the underlying principles of scientific thought (The Novum Organum), ones which he decided were fundamentally opposite to Aristotelian principles. Instead of Aristotle's "deduction" which he felt was only a way of arriving at conclusions on matters that were already known, he suggested a new method of "induction," or to put it another way, a method of observing universal laws at work on the basis of multiple observations of evidence. Furthermore he argued that the science that set out to discover these laws of nature should strive to be universal and abstract, so ascending "the ladder of the intellect."

Bacon takes credit for suggesting a discipline based on the investigation of causes which guided generation after generation of scientists, in particular the notion that the negative instance (i.e. when an experiment does *not* have an effect) was as important as the positive instance.

Mᴀʀᴄʜ

22

23

24

25

26

27

28

29

30

31

"A LITTLE PHILOSOPHY
INCLINETH MAN'S MIND TO
ATHEISM. BUT DEPTH IN
PHILOSOPHY BRINGETH MEN'S
MINDS ABOUT TO RELIGION"

FRANCIS BACON

JOURNAL

APRIL

1

2

3

4

5

6

7

RENÉ DESCARTES (1596-1650)

Descartes was a driving force behind the intellectual revolution of the seventeenth century, and is known as the father of modern philosophy. He was also a great mathematician. On the night of November 10th 1619 Descartes had a vision of the way he might construct a precise system of knowledge that could embrace all areas of human learning. This remained his project for the rest of his life.

While some of the arguments he used have come under criticism, Descartes' method has had an enormous influence on subsequent thought. Like Socrates, he decided to work out his own philosophy. Descartes was a mathematician and wanted to use the "mathematical method" even for philosophising. He set out to prove philosophical truths in the way one proves a mathematical theorem - by the use of reason, since only reason can give us certainty. It is far from certain, said Descartes, that we can rely on our senses.

"I THINK, THEREFORE I AM"

RENÉ DESCARTES

There seemed to be nothing of which he could be sure. But Descartes tried to work forward from this zero point. He doubted everything, and that was the only thing he was certain of. But now something struck him: one thing had to be true, and that was that he doubted. When he doubted, he had to be thinking, and because he was thinking, it had to be certain that he existed. Or, as he himself expressed it: Cogito, ergo sum. Which means "I think, therefore I am."

Descartes thought that minds and ideas were not physical things. The Englishman Thomas Hobbes, a contemporary of Descartes, completely disagreed. Hundreds of years after Descartes the mind/body debate is still a central problem of philosophy. Is the mind a purely physical thing? And if it is not, how can it interact with the physical body?

A PRIL

8

9

10

11

12

13

14

RENATVS CARTESIVS
Hagae Comitum.

Natus ex antiqua et nobili inter Pictones et Armoricos gente in Gallia.
ad militiam per Germaniam, et Pannoniam adolescens profectus, postea
per viginti annos in Batavia speculationibus indulgens, a Rege suo con,
ditionibus honorificis vocatus, et tandem a Christina Regina in Sueciam invitatus est.
Natus A. 1596. d. 31 Marty.   Den. A. 1680. d. 11 Febr.

PONCET·LE·PREVX·

"ONE CANNOT CONCEIVE ANYTHING SO STRANGE AND SO IMPLAUSIBLE THAT IT HAS NOT ALREADY BEEN SAID BY ONE PHILOSOPHER OR ANOTHER"

RENÉ DESCARTES

APRIL

15

16

17

18

19

20

21

"YOUR PHILOSOPHERS ARE ALWAYS TALKING ABOUT 'MAN' AND 'HUMANS' AND NOW IT'S ANOTHER TREATISE ON 'HUMAN NATURE.' It's as if this 'human' is a middle-aged man. I mean, life begins with pregnancy and birth, and I've heard nothing about nappies or crying babies so far. And hardly anything about love and friendship."

SOPHIE

BENEDICT DE SPINOZA (1632-1677)

Benedict (Baruch) de Spinoza came from a Jewish family who had fled to Holland from Portugal to escape the oppression of the Catholic Church. His whole life was to be subject to religious persecution.

He believed that Christianity and Judaism were kept alive by rigid dogma and ritual. He denied that the Bible was inspired by God down to the last letter, saying that when we read the Bible we must continually bear in mind the period in which it was written. He proposed a "critical" reading, which revealed a number of inconsistencies in the texts.

Spinoza said that everything is nature. He identified nature with God, saying that God is all, and all is in God. This is called pantheism. To Spinoza, God did not create the world in order to stand outside it. God is the world. So it follows that all our thoughts are also God's or nature's thoughts. There *is* only one God, one nature, or one Substance.

His philosophy is notoriously hard to understand. He was influenced by René Descartes but rejected his distinction of thought and matter as two separate substances, believing there was only one. Everything that exists can be reduced to one single reality which he simply called Substance.

Spinoza said that it was our passions - such as ambition and lust - which prevent us from achieving true happiness and harmony, but that if we recognise that everything happens from necessity, we can achieve an intuitive understanding of nature as a whole. We can come to realise with crystal clarity that everything is related, even that everything is One.

"ALL EXCELLENT THINGS ARE AS DIFFICULT AS THEY ARE RARE"

BENEDICT DE SPINOZA

The goal is to comprehend everything that exists in an all-embracing perception. Only then will we achieve true happiness and contentment. This was what Spinoza called seeing everything *"sub specie aeternitatis,"* which means to see everything from the perspective of eternity.

A PRIL

22

23

24

25

26

A PRIL

27

28

29

30

> ## "THE MIND'S INTELLECTUAL LOVE OF GOD IS PART OF THE INFINITE LOVE BY WHICH GOD LOVES HIMSELF"

BENEDICT DE SPINOZA

JOURNAL

_____

I will do what I can to acquaint you with your historical roots. It is the only way to become a human being. It is the only way to avoid floating in a vacuum."

ALBERTO

MAY

1

2

3

4

5

6

7

"At any rate we can be sure that what we see, hear, smell, and taste are the way we sense it."

SOPHIE

JOHN LOCKE (1632-1704)

One of the British Empiricists, John Locke lived at a time of great scientific discovery and political upheaval. He was to become deeply involved in, and affected by, both.

Locke's claim is that all our thoughts and ideas issue from what we have taken in through the senses. Before we perceive anything, the mind is a *"tabula rasa"* - or an empty slate, as bare and empty as a blackboard before the teacher arrives in the classroom. But then we begin to sense things. We see the world around us, we smell, taste, feel and hear. And nobody does this more intensely than an infant. In this way what Locke called "simple ideas of sense" arise. But the mind does not just passively receive information from outside it. Some activity happens in the mind as well. The single-sense ideas are worked on by thinking, reasoning, believing and doubting, thus giving rise to what he calls "reflection." So he distinguished between "sensation" and "reflection." The mind is not merely a passive receiver. It classifies and processes all sensations as they come streaming in.

Locke spoke out for intellectual liberty and tolerance. He was also preoccupied with equality of the sexes, maintaining that the subjugation of women to men was "man-made." Therefore it could be altered. He had a great influence on John Stuart Mill, who in turn had a key role in the struggle for equality of the sexes.

Locke was a forerunner of many liberal ideas which came into full flower later, during the French Enlightenment in the eighteenth century. It was he who first argued for the principle of division of powers, by which the power of the state is divided between different institutions: the legislative power, or elected representatives; the judicial power, or law courts; and the executive power, or the government. He rejected many of the ideas of the other great Empiricist, Thomas Hobbes (1588 - 1679) who believed in a powerful monarchy and that man has no right to rebel and break the "social contract."

Mʳ John Locke

MAY

8 _____

9 _____

10 _____

11 _____

12 _____

13 _____

"THE MIND IS
A BLANK PIECE
OF PAPER"

JOHN LOCKE

14 _____

_____

Title page of *Leviathan* by Thomas Hobbes

"WHEREVER
LAW ENDS,
TYRANNY
BEGINS"

JOHN LOCKE

M_AY_

15 _____

16 _____

17 _____

18 _____

19 _____

20 _____

21 _____

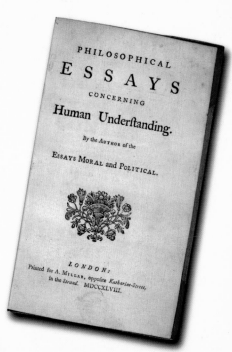

GOTTFRIED LEIBNIZ (1646-1716)

Born in Leipzig, Leibniz entered the service of the Baron of Boineburg and then that of the Duke of Brunswick in 1667.

Leibniz created a metaphysical theory to explain the nature of the world. It may not have been convincing but it certainly was imaginative. He thought that the world consisted of an infinite number of indivisible substances which he called monads. One of these monads was God, who made all the rest at the time of creation. The monads created by God were indestructible unless annihilated by Him. For Leibniz nothing existed except monads.

According to Leibniz God is all-powerful, all-knowing and all-good. In deciding what world to create He obviously had to create the very best possible one. That makes our world the very best of all possible worlds and Leibniz the greatest of all optimists! Voltaire's character Dr. Pangloss in his *Candide* was used to make merciless fun of him for this. If this is the best of all possible worlds, there is no real evil. As Leibniz saw it, if you try to imagine some slight improvement in some aspect of this world, you will find that this improvement can only be achieved at the cost of making things worse elsewhere.

Leibniz's diplomatic duties sent him to Paris from 1672 to 1676. Here he encountered a great wealth of ideas and people that stimulated and influenced his thought.

As well as becoming familiar with Cartesian philosophy he met the physicist Huygens who recognised and developed Leibniz's immense talent as a mathematician. It was during this period that Leibniz invented the infinitesimal calculus, not knowing that Newton had done so at the same time. Great animosity sprang up between the two over whose work was the original.

Gottfried Wilhelm von Leibniz.

Geb. im Juli, nach Andern im Jan. 1646 zu Leipzig, gest. d. 14. Nov. 1716 zu Hannover.

Einer der umfassendsten und geistreichsten Gelehrten des 17ten Jahrhunderts, besonders hervorragend als Mathematiker durch Erfindung der Differentialrechnung und als Philosoph durch eine Lehre, welche, von Christian Wolf in systematische Form gebracht, lange Zeit die vorherrschende in Deutschland war. Der Grundgedanke ist, daß allem wahrhaft Seienden, auch in der geistigen Welt, letzte einfache Wesenheiten, die Monaden, zu Grunde liegen, die nach einer von Gott, der ursprünglichen Monas, prästabilirten Harmonie das Princip ihrer Veränderungen in sich tragen. In seiner Theodicee stellte Leibniz einen vernünftigen, keineswegs mit passivem Quietismus zu verwechselnden Optimismus auf.

M AY

22

23

24

25

26

27

28

"**M**aterial can be broken up into smaller and smaller bits, but the soul cannot even be divided into two."

ALBERTO

"IT IS ONE OF MY MOST IMPORTANT AND BEST VERIFIED MAXIMS THAT NATURE MAKES NO LEAPS. THIS I HAVE CALLED THE LAW OF CONTINUITY"

GOTTFRIED LEIBNIZ

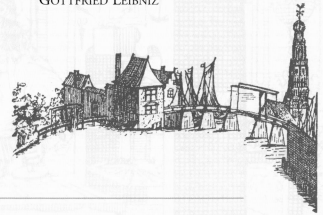

29 _____

30 _____

31 _____

JOURNAL

_____

_____

_____

_____

_____

_____

_____

_____

"I OFTEN SAY A GREAT DOCTOR
KILLS MORE PEOPLE THAN A
GREAT GENERAL"

GOTTFRIED LEIBNIZ

JUNE

1

2

3

4

5

6

7

D.ʳ GEORGE BERKELEY,
Biſhop of Cloyne.

GEORGE BERKELEY (1685-1753)

George Berkeley was born in Kilkenny in Ireland. When he was just 15 he went to Trinity College, Dublin, to study philosophy, science and theology. Here he immersed himself in the ideas of Descartes, Locke, Hobbes, Boyle and Newton. Within a few years he had formulated the idealist philosophy that he was to hold for the rest of his life.

He took Locke's ideas one step further: He said the only things that exist are those we perceive. But we do not perceive "material" or "matter." We do not perceive things as tangible objects. To assume that what we perceive has its own underlying "substance" is jumping to conclusions. We have absolutely no experience on which to base such a claim.

According to Berkeley, your own soul can be the cause of your own ideas - just as when you dream - but only another will or spirit can be the cause of the ideas that make up the "corporeal" world. Everything is due to that spirit which is the cause of "everything in everything" and in which, he said, "all things consist."

Berkeley was of course thinking of God. He said that "we can moreover claim that the existence of God is far more clearly perceived than the existence of man."

"WE HAVE FIRST RAISED A DUST THEN COMPLAIN WE CANNOT SEE"

GEORGE BERKELEY

Everything we see and feel is "an effect of God's power." For God is "intimately present in our consciousness, causing to exist for us the profusion of ideas and perceptions that we are constantly subject to." The whole world around us and our whole life exist in God. He is the one cause of everything that exists. We exist only in the mind of God.

In 1728 he went to Rhode Island in America, attempting to set up a missionary college in Bermuda, but the project never got off the ground. In 1731 he returned and became Bishop of Cloyne in 1734.

JUNE

8 _____

9 _____

10 _____

11 _____

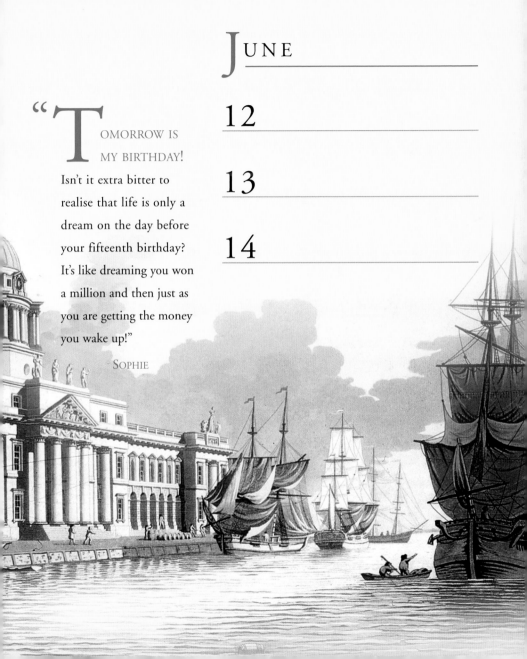

JUNE

12

13

14

"TOMORROW IS MY BIRTHDAY! Isn't it extra bitter to realise that life is only a dream on the day before your fifteenth birthday? It's like dreaming you won a million and then just as you are getting the money you wake up!"

SOPHIE

JUNE

15

16

17

18

19

"WESTWARD THE COURSE OF EMPIRE TAKES ITS WAY"

GEORGE BERKELEY

Y ou are hereby invited to a philosophical garden party at 3 Clover Close on Saturday June 23rd (Midsummer Eve) at 7pm. During the evening we shall hopefully solve the mystery of life. Please bring warm sweaters and bright ideas suitable for solving the riddles of philosophy.

JOANNA INGEBRIGTSEN AND SOPHIE AMUNDSEN

JUNE

20

21

22

23

VOLTAIRE (1694-1778)

Voltaire (the pseudonym of François-Marie Arouet), while contributing little that could be described as entirely original to the philosophical canon, poured out to the world a most extraordinary mixture of novels, plays, reviews, pamphlets and historical works. In many ways, with his total commitment to the world around him, he was the epitome of the Age of Enlightenment.

Voltaire's early satirical works earned him a year in the Bastille and later, in 1726, exile to England. Already a radical and liberal, he quickly saw in England a society that enjoyed far greater justice and freedom than France. In his *Lettres Philosophiques* he praises social, religious and political liberty and uses social utility as the definition of good political institutions.

He was a firm believer in God, but was entirely opposed to the views of the Church and proposed that doubt should be the beginning of wisdom and enlightenment. He saw evil as essentially man-made, and a mystery that refused to be solved.

His most famous tale, *Candide,* highlights a world where human life and dignity are of little importance. Voltaire's portrait of Pangloss in the novel was at the expense of Pope and Leibnitz.

Voltaire, unlike many of his supporters, was a strong advocator of non-violence and believed with passion that the fight against authority, tradition and conformity could be won without the spilling of blood. Although he died before the onset of the French Revolution, his style of thought did much to inspire the events of 1789.

"WORK KEEPS US FROM THREE GREAT EVILS: BOREDOM, VICE AND POVERTY"

VOLTAIRE

J UNE

24

25

26

27

28

29

30

JOURNAL

"LIBERTY OF THOUGHT IS THE LIFE OF THE SOUL"

VOLTAIRE

JULY

1

2

3

4

5

6

7

WHERE DOES
THE WORLD
COME FROM? the note said...
I don't know, Sophie thought,
Surely nobody really knows.
And yet... Sophie thought it
was a fair question. For the
first time in her life she felt
it wasn't right to live in the
world without at least
inquiring where the world
came from.

SOPHIE

DAVID HUME (1711-1776)

Born in Edinburgh, Hume published his most important work *"A treatise of Human Nature"* when he was only 28.

As an Empiricist, Hume took it upon himself to clean up all the woolly concepts and thought constructions that previous philosophers had invented. There were piles of old wreckage left from the Middle Ages and the rationalist philosophy of the seventeenth century. Hume proposed the return to our spontaneous experience of the world. No philosopher, he said,

wings and human figures separately. So, according to Hume, an "angel" is a complex idea. It consists of two different experiences which are not in fact related, but which nevertheless are associated in man's imagination. Leading on from this, Hume believed that "God" was a complex idea we paste together in our minds.

Hume rejected any attempt to prove the existence of God. This is not to say that he ruled out the possibility that God exists; he thought, however, that to try to prove religious faith by human reason was nonsense. Hume was not a Christian, neither was he a confirmed atheist. He was what we call an agnostic - someone who holds that the existence of God can neither be proved nor disproved. When Hume was dying, a friend asked him if he believed in life after death. He is said to have answered: "It is also possible that a knob of coal placed upon the fire will not burn."

"BE A PHILOSOPHER; BUT AMIDST ALL YOUR PHILOSOPHY, BE STILL A MAN"

DAVID HUME

"will ever be able to take us behind the daily experiences or give us rules of conduct that are different from those we get through reflections on everyday life."

In the time of Hume there was a widespread belief in angels. That is, human figures with wings. No one has ever actually seen such a creature, yet everybody has at one time seen

Hume himself believed that everything had a cause and that there were regularities in the world (laws of nature) which would continue to hold. But the fact that one thing follows after another thus does not necessarily mean there is a causal link.

Ironically, by denying these "causal links," Hume ended up by undermining the basic tenets of Empiricism, the very movement of which he was a leader.

JULY

8 _____

9 _____

10 _____

11 _____

12 _____

July

13 _____

14 _____

"ERRORS IN RELIGION ARE DANGEROUS, THOSE IN PHILOSOPHY ONLY RIDICULOUS"

DAVID HUME

"THE LIFE OF MAN IS OF NO GREATER IMPORTANCE TO THE UNIVERSE THAT THAT OF AN OYSTER"

DAVID HUME

JULY

15

16

17

18

19

20

21

22

Immanuel Kant (1724-1804)

Kant became Professor of Logic and Metaphysics at the University of Königsberg in 1770 and taught there for most of his life. He was also greatly interested in science and published works on astronomy and geophysics.

Unlike the empiricists, Kant thought that the mind of man is not just "passive wax" which simply receives sensations from outside. The mind actively shapes the way we apprehend the world. What we see, taste, hear, smell and feel doesn't just depend on what is outside us but what is inside us, and on the way our reason shapes our sensations.

Kant called this the Copernican Revolution in the problem of human knowledge. By this he meant that his ideas were just as new and just as radically different from earlier beliefs as when Copernicus claimed that the earth revolved around the sun.

Kant's greatest contribution to philosophy is the dividing line he draws between things in themselves - *das Ding-an-sich* - and things as they appear to us.

We can never have certain knowledge of things "in themselves." We can only know how things "appear" to us. On the other hand, prior to any particular experience we can say something about how things will be perceived by the human mind.

All the philosophical systems before Hegel had one thing in common, namely, the attempt to set up eternal criteria for what man can know about the world. Kant's approach to this problem was to make a distinction between the world as it appears to us and the world as it is in itself. He thought that we can only have knowledge of the world as it appears, and we can never know the absolute truths about the world as it is in itself.

"THE MAJESTY OF DUTY HAS NOTHING TO DO WITH THE ENJOYMENT OF LIFE"

IMMANUEL KANT

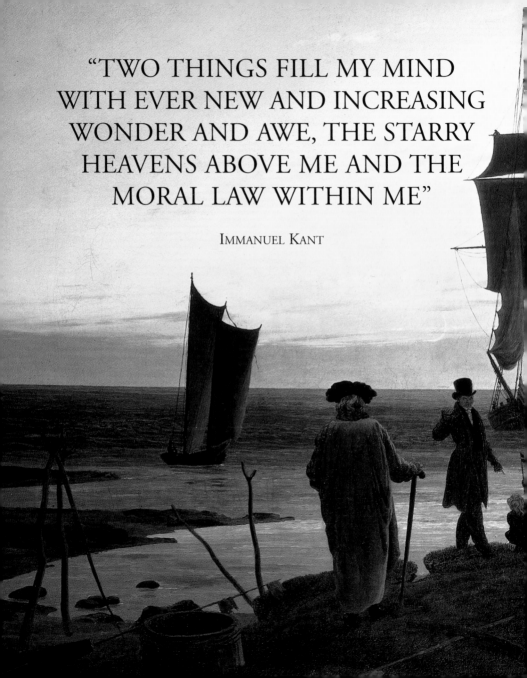

"TWO THINGS FILL MY MIND
WITH EVER NEW AND INCREASING
WONDER AND AWE, THE STARRY
HEAVENS ABOVE ME AND THE
MORAL LAW WITHIN ME"

IMMANUEL KANT

J ULY

23

24

25

26

27

28

29

30

31

JOURNAL

The difference between schoolteachers and philosophers is that schoolteachers think they know a lot of stuff that they try and force down our throats. Philosophers try and figure things out with the pupils.

SOPHIE

AUGUST

1

2

3

4

5

6

7

> "Long before the child learns to talk properly, and long before it learns to think philosophically, the world will have become a habit.
>
> ...A PITY IF YOU ASK ME."
>
> ALBERTO

GEORG WILHELM FRIEDRICH HEGEL
(1770-1831)

Georg Wilhelm Friedrich Hegel was born in Stuttgart, Germany. In 1816 he became a professor in Heidelberg, the centre of German National Romanticism. in 1818 he was given the prestigious post of Professor of Philosophy at Berlin University, just at the time when the city was becoming the spiritual centre of Europe.

He united and developed most of the ideas that surfaced in the Romantic period, but he was sharply critical of many of the Romantics. Schelling, as well as other Romantics, had said that the deepest meaning of life lay in what they called the "world spirit." Hegel also uses the term "world spirit," but in a new sense. When Hegel talks of "world spirit" or "world reason," he means the sum of human utterances, because only man has a "spirit."

Because something new is always being added as philosophy develops through history, reason is progressive. In other words, human knowledge is constantly expanding and progressing towards an ever increasing knowledge of itself. It's the same with rivers - they become broader and broader as they get nearer to the sea. So while neither Plato's philosophy nor Kant's is totally correct, Kant's is more right than Plato's says Hegel.

The world spirit, says Hegel, reaches the highest form of self-realisation in absolute spirit. And this absolute spirit is art, religion and philosophy. And of these, philosophy is the highest form of knowledge because in philosophy the world spirit reflects on its own impact on history.

Hegel's impact on his contemporaries was immense, as is his influence on modern philosophers.

AUGUST

8

9

10

11

12

13

14

15

AUGUST

16 _____

17 _____

18 _____

19 _____

"TO HIM WHO LOOKS AT THE
WORLD RATIONALLY THE WORLD
LOOKS RATIONALLY BACK. THE
RELATIONSHIP IS MUTUAL"

GEORG HEGEL

"WE MAY AFFIRM ABSOLUTELY THAT NOTHING GREAT IN THE WORLD HAS BEEN ACCOMPLISHED WITHOUT PASSION"

GEORG HEGEL

20

21

22

CHARLES DARWIN (1809-1882)

Charles Robert Darwin was born in Shrewsbury, England. From an early age Charles was fascinated by the natural world. After finishing his studies at Cambridge, Darwin was asked to accompany a government ship, *HMS Beagle*, on a two-year voyage to survey the coast of South America. The voyage was the most significant event of Darwin's life. He managed to examine and collect a great many undiscovered species, and for this alone he became renowned as a scientist on his return to Britain. More importantly, as a result of these observations Darwin came to formulate his theory of evolution and the idea of "natural selection." *The Origin of Species* was published in 1859 and *The Descent of Man* in 1871.

In the former he postulated that it was due to natural selection in the struggle for life that those who were best adapted to their surroundings would survive and perpetuate the race. He further proposed that the struggle for survival is frequently hardest among species that resemble each other the most. They have to fight for the same food. There, the slightest advantage - that is to say, the infinitesimal variation - truly comes into its own. The more bitter the struggle for survival, the quicker will be the evolution of new species, so that only the very best adapted will survive and the others will die out.

In *The Descent of Man* he drew attention to the great similarities between humans and animals, advancing the theory that men and anthropoid apes must at one time have evolved from the same progenitor.

The essence of Darwin's theory was that utterly random variations had finally produced Man. As if it wasn't bad enough that he claimed we are related to apes, Darwin had turned Man into a product of something as unsentimental as the struggle for existence. Many people found this view difficult to accept.

> "I HAVE CALLED THIS PRINCIPLE, BY WHICH EACH SLIGHT VARIATION, IF USEFUL, IS PRESERVED, BY THE TERM NATURAL SELECTION"
>
> CHARLES DARWIN

AUGUST

23

24

25

26

27

28

"Wasn't there a connection between the development of ideas and science on the one hand and the greenhouse effect and deforestation on the other? *Maybe it was not so crazy to call man's thirst for knowledge a fall from grace?*"

HILDE

AUGUST

29 _____

30 _____

31 _____

JOURNAL

"MAN WITH ALL HIS NOBLE QUALITIES... WITH HIS GODLIKE
INTELLECT WHICH HAS PENETRATED INTO THE MOVEMENTS
AND CONSTITUTION OF THE SOLAR SYSTEM... STILL BEARS IN HIS
BODILY FRAME THE INDELIBLE STAMP OF HIS LOWLY ORIGIN"

CHARLES DARWIN

SEPTEMBER

1 _____

2 _____

3 _____

4 _____

I HAVE TO ADMIT THAT I AM
NOT ALTOGETHER CONVINCED
OF THE IMMORTALITY OF THE SOUL.
Personally, I have no recollections
from my former lives. If you could
convince me that my deceased
Grandmother's soul is happy in the
world of ideas I would be grateful.

SOPHIE

5 _____

6 _____

7 _____

SØREN KIERKEGAARD (1813-1855)

Danish by birth, Kierkegaard is the first important existentialist philosopher. A passionate, religious man with a melancholic tendency, Kierkegaard was a brilliant and witty writer. His work reflected his intense character and the deeply personal nature of philosophy as he saw it. Kierkegaard was a savage critic of the impersonality of Hegelianism and the Romantic movement. His attacks on society and "Sunday Christianity" were also scathing. He wanted people to make decisions, evaluate beliefs, and decide what is true for themselves, rather than absolving themselves from any responsibility to do so.

According to Kierkegaard, rather than searching for the Truth with a capital T, it is more important to find the kind of truths that are meaningful to the individual's life - "the truth for me." He thus sets the individual, or "each and every man," up against the "system." Kierkegaard thought Hegel had forgotten that he was a man.

Toward the end of his life, especially, Kierkegaard became aggressively critical of society, declaring that "the whole of Europe is on the road to bankruptcy." He believed he was living in an age utterly devoid of passion and commitment.

Kierkegaard believed that there were three different forms of life: the aesthetic stage, where a person lives wholly in the world of the senses, and is a slave to his own desires and moods; the ethical stage, characterised by seriousness and consistency of moral choices; and finally the religious stage, which to Kierkegaard was, of course, Christianity.

And although it can be "terrible to jump into the open arms of the living God," as Kierkegaard put it, it is the only path to redemption.

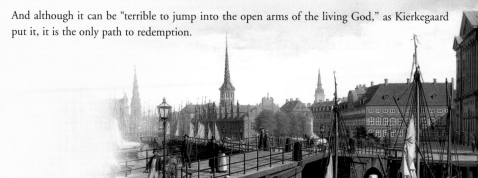

"LIFE MUST BE UNDERSTOOD BACKWARDS, BUT LIVED FORWARDS"

SØREN KIERKEGAARD

"EXPERIENCE, IT IS SAID, MAKES A
MAN WISE. THAT IS VERY SILLY
TALK. IF THERE WERE NOTHING
BEYOND EXPERIENCE IT WOULD
SIMPLY DRIVE HIM MAD"

SØREN KIERKEGAARD

SEPTEMBER

8 _____

9 _____

10 _____

11 _____

12 _____

13 _____

14 _____

*"The only thing we
require to be good
philosophers is the
faculty of wonder."*

Alberto

SEPTEMBER

15

16

17

18

19

20

21

KARL MARX (1818-1883)

Marx was not only a philosopher but a historian, sociologist and economist. No other philosopher has had greater significance on everyday practical politics: however we should be wary of identifying everything that calls itself Marxism with Marx's own thinking. Indeed his essential beliefs have often been substantially altered in the 20th century to suit the ideas of particular political credos. We should also remember that his friend and colleague Engels contributed much to what was subsequently known as Marxism.

To both Marx and Hegel work was a positive thing and closely connected with the essence of mankind. A person who was unemployed was, in a sense, empty. However, under the capitalist system the worker labours for someone else. His labour is thus something external and the worker becomes alien to both his work and to himself–which Marx found unacceptable.

The first sentence of 'The Communist Manifesto' (1848) says: "A spectre is haunting Europe–the spectre of Communism." This clearly frightened the bourgeoisie–the social class which, to Marx's way of thinking, treated the workers as 'slaves'.

Marx believed that there were a number of inherent contradictions in the capitalist method of production–principally, that because of a lack of rational control, the system would self-destruct. Self-destruction would lead to revolution and thence to the "dictatorship of the proletariat" a society in which the means of production were owned by the people themselves.

Today economists can establish that Marx was mistaken on a number of vital issues, not least his analysis of the crisis of capitalism. However, the fact that Europe today has a more just society than in Marx's time, is due not least to Marx himself and to the socialist movement which he inspired.

"HISTORY REPEATS ITSELF – FIRST AS
TRAGEDY, THE SECOND TIME AS FARCE"

KARL MARX

SEPTEMBER

22

23

24

25

26

27

SEPTEMBER

28 _____

29 _____

30 _____

"RELIGION IS THE SIGH OF THE
OPPRESSED CREATURE, THE
HEART OF A HEARTLESS WORLD,
JUST AS IT IS THE SPIRIT OF
SPIRITLESS CONDITIONS. IT IS THE
OPIUM OF THE PEOPLE"

KARL MARX

J OURNAL

"THE HISTORY OF ALL HITHERTO
EXISTING SOCIETY IS THE HISTORY
OF CLASS STRUGGLES"

KARL MARX

OCTOBER

1 _____

2 _____

3 _____

4 _____

5 _____

6 _____

7 _____

FRIEDRICH NIETZSCHE (1844-1900)

Friedrich Nietzsche was born in 1844 near Leipzig, where his father was a minister. From the age of 24 he taught classical philology at the University of Basel in Switzerland. While at Basel, he was a friend of the composer Richard Wagner and his brilliant wife Cosima. Nietzsche defended Wagner's controversial music with writings on the theory of art, but for reasons that are not fully known he broke with Wagner in connection with the opening of the festival at Bayreuth in 1876.

His main works were jotted down as notes, reflections and aphorisms in short periods of relief between painful headaches and other mental attacks. His deep pessimism about human life probably owes something to his persistently bad health.

Nietzsche believed that the experience of great art was the meaning of existence. For this reason he idolised Greek tragedy and despised philosophies that attempted to rationalise life and morality. Nietzsche proposed a "master morality" that would celebrate strong and creative personalities, to replace Christianity's "slave morality." He wanted people to reach their full creative potential without being hampered by questions of an afterlife or other realms. Nietzsche was influenced by Darwin's ideas of man as descended from beasts, though he thought that the basic urge of man was not one of self-preservation but of conquest.

Nietzsche's most important philosophical works are *The Birth of Tragedy* (1872), *Beyond Good and Evil* (1886), *On the Genealogy of Morals* (1887) and *The Will to Power* (1901). He was also a poet as can be seen in *Thus Spoke Zarathustra* (1882-85). There he formulates his teaching of "God is dead," "superman," "love of fate" and "the eternal recurrence of all things."

Finally, it should be stressed that Nietzsche was not anti-semitic, despite the attempt by the National Socialist Party to adopt him as an apologist.

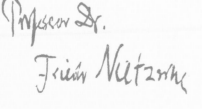

"MAN IS A ROPE, TIED BETWEEN
BEAST AND SUPERMAN – A ROPE
OVER AN ABYSS"

Friedrich Nietzsche

OCTOBER

8

9

10

11

12

13

14

"THOUGHTS ARE THE SHADOWS OF OUR FEELINGS – ALWAYS DARKER, EMPTIER AND SIMPLER"

FRIEDRICH NIETZSCHE

ALSO
SPRACH
ZARATHUSTRA

FRIEDRICH
NIETZSCHE

OCTOBER

15

16

17

"A white rabbit is pulled out of a top hat. Because it is an extremely large rabbit the trick takes many billions of years."

ALBERTO

OCTOBER

18

19

20

21

"I TELL YOU: ONE MUST HAVE
CHAOS IN ONESELF, TO GIVE
BIRTH TO A DANCING STAR"

FRIEDRICH NIETZSCHE

SIGMUND FREUD (1856-1939)

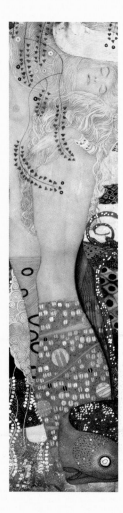

Sigmund Freud was born in a town called Freiberg in the part of the Austro-Hungarian Empire that later became Czechoslovakia. After graduation he became a doctor at the Vienna General Hospital and developed a special interest in mental illness. He learned how to use hypnosis as a clinical technique and started to think about formulating his ideas into a theory of the mind.

Freud is regarded more as a psychologist than a philosopher. His work is, however, significant to philosophy in that it has advanced our understanding of the mind.

Freud held that there is a constant tension between man and his surroundings. In particular, there is a conflict between his drives or needs and the demands of society. Our actions are not always guided by reason. Irrational impulses often determine what we think, what we dream, and what we do. Such irrational impulses can be an expression of basic drives or needs. This in itself was not a new discovery. But Freud showed that these basic needs can be disguised or "sublimated," thereby controlling our actions without our being aware of it.

Freud also coined the expressions Id, Ego and SuperEgo. When we are first born into the world, we live out our physical and mental needs directly and unashamedly. This is the pleasure principle or Id. But gradually we learn to regulate our desires and adjust to our surroundings. In Freud's terms, we develop an Ego which has this regulative function.

Finally, from infancy we are constantly faced with the moral demands of our parents and of society. Even when we are grown up, we retain the echo of such moral demands and judgments. Freud called this part of our mental make-up the SuperEgo.

OCTOBER

22 _____

23 _____

24 _____

25 _____

"**M**OST
RESPECTED PHILOSOPHER,
your generous correspondence
course in philosophy is greatly
appreciated by us here. But
it bothers us not to know who
you are. We therefore request
you use your full name. In
return come and have coffee
with us. I am also very good
at making coffee."

SOPHIE

26 _____

27 _____

28 _____

> "THE PSYCHIC DEVELOPMENT OF THE INDIVIDUAL IS A SHORT REPETITION OF THE COURSE OF DEVELOPMENT OF THE HUMAN RACE"

SIGMUND FREUD

29 _____

30 _____

31 _____

JOURNAL

"RELIGION IS AN ILLUSION AND IT
DERIVES ITS STRENGTH FROM ITS
READINESS TO FIT IN WITH OUR
INSTINCTUAL WISHFUL IMPULSES"

SIGMUND FREUD

NOVEMBER

1

2

3

4

5

6

"FEAR IS THE MAIN SOURCE OF
SUPERSTITION, AND ONE OF THE
MAIN SOURCES OF CRUELTY. TO
CONQUER FEAR IS THE BEGINNING
OF WISDOM"

BERTRAND RUSSELL

BERTRAND RUSSELL (1872-1970)

Bertrand Russell came from a distinguished aristocratic family (he became the third Earl Russell in 1931, taking his seat in the House of Lords representing the Labour party). He read mathematics at Trinity College, Cambridge, but later switched to philosophy. He became a fellow at the university in 1895, was a lecturer from 1910 to 1916, but was sacked in 1918 for pacifistic agitation and imprisoned for six months because of his beliefs. In 1944 he was re-elected as a fellow of Trinity. Russell was perhaps one of the most famous pacifists ever, and in later years he became one of the founders of the Campaign For Nuclear Disarmament. His fighting against warfare, inhumanity and injustice saw results such as the Russell Tribunal, which accused US politicians of war crimes during the Vietnam war.

His first book appeared in 1897 and dealt with the foundations of geometry. However, it was his *Principia Mathematica* (1910–1913), written in conjunction with A.N. Whitehead, that became his Magnum Opus. Indeed many people think this to be the greatest work on logic since Aristotle. From mathematics he went on to write a whole series of philosophical books, many of which were written with an eye for the beginner in the subject, the most well-known and widespread being *The Wisdom of the West* (1959). In his books he attempted to apply his ideas on the use of logic to philosophy, and he pioneered a development later known as "analytic philosophy."

> "I SAY QUITE DELIBERATELY THAT THE CHRISTIAN RELIGION, AS ORGANISED IN ITS CHURCHES, HAS BEEN AND STILL IS THE PRINCIPAL ENEMY OF MORAL PROGRESS IN THE WORLD"
>
> BERTRAND RUSSELL

Russell, Nobel Prize winner in literature, author of 60 books, among them his astonishing and lively autobiography, spokesman for scientific co-operation between east and west, lived to be close to 100. This most influential intellectual of the 20th century had a life so full of scientific, social and political engagement, it could have been enough for a millennium.

NOVEMBER

7

8

9

10

" I am out of one of Grimm's fairy tales.
That was nearly two hundred years ago...
"and where are you from?"
"We're out of a book on philosophy."
"I am the philosophy teacher and this is my student, Sophie"
"Hee hee, that's a new one!"

SOPHIE'S WORLD

" THREE PASSIONS, SIMPLE BUT
OVERWHELMINGLY STRONG,
HAVE GOVERNED MY LIFE: THE
LONGING FOR LOVE, THE
SEARCH FOR KNOWLEDGE,
AND UNBEARABLE PITY FOR
THE SUFFERING OF MANKIND"

BERTRAND RUSSELL

11

12

13

14

November

15

16

17

18

19

20

21

22

"MATHEMATICS, RIGHTLY VIEWED, POSSESSES NOT ONLY TRUTH, BUT SUPREME BEAUTY - A BEAUTY COLD AND AUSTERE, LIKE THAT OF SCULPTURE, WITHOUT APPEAL TO ANY PART OF OUR WEAKER NATURE, WITHOUT THE GORGEOUS TRAPPINGS OF PAINTING OR MUSIC, YET SUBLIMELY PURE, AND CAPABLE OF A STERN PERFECTION SUCH AS ONLY THE GREATEST ART CAN SHOW"

BERTRAND RUSSELL

Martin Heidegger (1889-1976)

Heidegger was one of the most vital and prolific thinkers of the twentieth century. After the Great War of 1914-1918 the problems of human life were discussed with new intensity. Most people felt that the old world was gone for ever. The belief in progress was brushed aside. Traditional humanism, liberalism and optimism were regarded with suspicion. Unfortunately he was one of the very few great intellectuals between the wars who were attracted to Nazism.

Heidegger intended to give an objective, scientific presentation of the condition of man as it appears to us. He wished to analyse the experience of human life and to disclose "the meaning of Being." In *Being and Time* he claims that temporality is the distinctive feature of all parts of the condition of man. No part of a human being is standing over or outside the passing of time. Heidegger asserts that human beings are identical with their actual existence. The essence of man is nothing more than his fleeting and passing existence. From this line of reasoning it is impossible to see Heidegger as perhaps the first atheist existentialist. He certainly had a huge influence on Sartre.

No other thinker has presented man's finite condition as mercilessly as does Heidegger. Death, decay, transitoriness, in other words "finiteness," are present in everything we think and do. Heidegger's point is that man is not something that unfortunately has to die. Death is not something that happens to man as a surprise or something to avoid. Death is founded on the tyranny of time itself, a power that nobody can escape.

Heidegger also paints a picture of the development of western metaphysics as a catastrophe. The process of "oblivion of Being" *(Seinsvergessenheit)* has been victorious. He said that Ancient Greek philosophy was already a failure that prepared for the conquests of modern technology and the modern adoration of power.

In his later years Heidegger was occupied with eastern thinking as he tried to find alternatives to the western "oblivion of Being."

Nᴏᴠᴇᴍʙᴇʀ

23 _____

24 _____

25 _____

26 _____

27 _____

28 _____

29 _____

30 _____

"WHATEVER
AND HOWEVER
WE MAY TRY TO
THINK, WE
THINK WITHIN
THE SPHERE OF
TRADITION"

Mᴀʀᴛɪɴ Hᴇɪᴅᴇɢɢᴇʀ

JOURNAL

DECEMBER

1 _____

2 _____

3 _____

4 _____

5 _____

6 _____

7 _____

8 _____

9 _____

LUDWIG WITTGENSTEIN (1889-1951)

Wittgenstein, born in Vienna, showed an early flair for engineering and in 1908 went to Manchester University, England, to study aeronautics. Here he developed a deep interest in the foundations of mathematics and went on to Cambridge to study under Bertrand Russell.

For Wittgenstein the central topic of philosophy was language. He wanted to know what meaning was and how we could mean anything by language.

He said that philosophical problems arise because we fail to understand language. The only proper role for the philosopher is to be a therapist who seeks to dissolve philosophical problems by looking at how we actually use language. Traditional philosophical problems "arise when language goes on holiday." Philosophers who do not focus on language as it is actually used are like flies hopelessly buzzing in a bottle: "What is your aim in philosophy? To show the fly the way out of the bottle."

Wittgenstein committed himself to a very extreme form of relativism, (the doctrine that there is not a single truth or reality). What is true and what really exists is relative to different cultures or different historical periods. He remarks in the *Philosophical Investigations* that if a lion could talk we could not understand him. That is, the lion's talking would be part of a form of life so different from us that we could not make sense of it. The lion would have its own conceptions of reality, and who is to say who is right?

He was something of an eccentric. Bertrand Russell reported that he apparently lived on milk and vegetables only, and was constantly talking of committing suicide (three of his brothers had done so). Russell remarks that he never asked Wittgenstein to leave his room, even if he had paced silently until 3 in the morning, for fear that he would kill himself.

He lectured in a deckchair and ordered his students to bring their own.

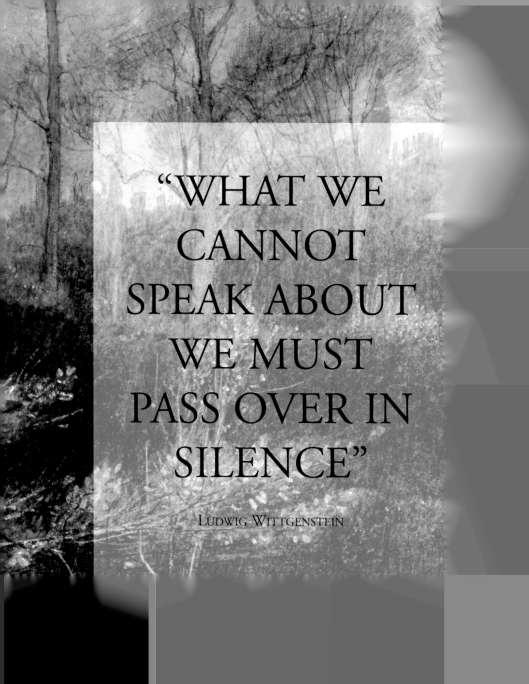

DECEMBER

10

11

12

13

14

15

16

17 _____

18 _____

19 _____

20 _____

21 _____

22 _____

"IF A LION COULD
TALK, WE COULD NOT
UNDERSTAND HIM"

LUDWIG WITTGENSTEIN

JEAN-PAUL SARTRE (1905-1980)

Born in Paris, as well as publishing readable and popular philosophical works Sartre was also a successful playwright, novelist, political commentator and literary critic.

"EVERYTHING IS GRATUITOUS, THIS GARDEN, THIS CITY AND MYSELF. WHEN YOU SUDDENLY REALISE IT, IT MAKES YOU FEEL SICK AND EVERYTHING BEGINS TO DRIFT . . . THAT'S NAUSEA"

JEAN-PAUL SARTRE

When the Second World War broke out Sartre joined the French army. In 1940 he was captured by the Germans and imprisoned for a year before being returned to occupied France. The war changed Sartre, and his concern shifted from academic philosophy to the problems of the human condition. His great work *Being and Nothingness* was published in 1943, followed by *Existentialism and Humanism* in 1945. Both were immediately popular.

Sartre said that man's existence takes priority over whatever he might otherwise be. "Existence takes priority over essence." By essence we mean that which something consists of - the nature, or being, of something. But according to Sartre, man has no such innate "nature." Man must therefore create himself. He must create his own nature or "essence," because it is not fixed in advance.

When people realise they are alive and will one day die - and there is no meaning in life to cling to - they experience angst, Sartre said. Man feels alien in a world without meaning. When he describes man's "alienation," he is echoing the central ideas of Hegel and Marx. Man's feeling of alienation in the world creates a sense of despair, boredom, nausea and absurdity. "Man is condemned to be free," Sartre said. On the other hand our freedom obliges us to make something of ourselves, to live "authentically" or "truly."

"MAN IS CONDEMNED TO BE FREE"

JEAN-PAUL SARTRE

DECEMBER

23

24

25

26

27

28

29

30

31

J OURNAL

"WE DO NOT DO WHAT WE WANT
AND YET WE ARE RESPONSIBLE
FOR WHAT WE ARE"

JEAN-PAUL SARTRE

ACKNOWLEDGEMENTS

Title Page: A Portrait of a Philosopher, British Library (BL). January: Panathenaic Amphora, British Museum (BM). Roman Marble bust, Townley Collection. Democritus by Antoine Coypel (B). Detail from Emperor Julian and his Wife, British Museum (BM). Shipwreck; Socrates and others, British Library (BL). Socrates, Marble Head by Lysippus, Louvre (B). Socrates and a Stag by J.B. Port, British Library (BL). February: Luna Marble Head of Plato: Fitzwilliam Museum (B). School of Athens by Raphael, Vatican (B). Aristotle Engraving, Private Collection (B). Marble Head of Aristotle, Kunsthistorisches Museum, Vienna (B). The Young Aristotle by Charles Degeorge, Musée d'Orsay (B). March: St. Augustine in his cell by S. Boticelli, Uffizi (B). Vision of St. Augustine by Vitore Carpaccio, Scuola di San Giorgio, Venice (B). Francis Bacon by Paul van Somer, Private Collection (B). Portrait of Francis Bacon by William Marshall Stapleton, Private Collection (B). April: Meditationes de Prima Philosophia, Title Page (AKG). René Descartes by Sebastien Bourdon, Louvre (B). Portrait of René Descartes by Frans Hals, Private Collection (B). Benedict Spinoza by A. de Beaulieu (ME). May: John Locke by S. Brounower (ME). Portrait of John Locke by Sir Godfrey Kneller, Philip Moull Historical Portraits Ltd, London (B). Frontispiece to Leviathan, Private Collection (B). Philosophical Essays, Title Page, British Library (BL). Portrait of Gottfried Wilhelm Leibniz, German School 18th Century, (B). June: Berkeley by Anon, Universal Magazine (ME). George Berkeley by John Smybert (B). Custom House, Dublin by James Malton, Stapleton Collection (B). Portrait of Voltaire by Nicolas de Largillière, Private (B). Hope the Game Finishes Soon, Musée Carnavalet, Paris (B). La Chasse aux Aristocrates, Private Collection (B). July: David Hume by Louis Carrogis, Scottish National Portrait Gallery (B). View from the top of Calton Hill, City of Edinburgh Museums and Art Galleries (B). The Stages of Life by Caspar David Friedrich, Museum der Bildende Kunste, Leipzig (B). August: Frontispiece to The Celestial Atlas, Private Collection (B). Portrait of Georg Wilhelm Friedrich Hegel by Jacob Schlesinger, Nationalgalerie, Berlin (B). Die Nieuwe groote lichtende Zee, British Library (BL). Charles Darwin by Julia Margaret Cameron, Private Collection (B). Origin of Species, Title Page, Natural History Museum, London (B). Professor Darwin, English School, 19th Century, Natural History Museum, London (B). September: Copenhagen by Heinrich Hansen, Christie's Images (B). Søren Kierkegaard (HG). Winter Landscape at Copenhagen by Paul Gauguin, Private Collection (B). A Strike at Saint Ouen by R.L. Delance, Musée d'Orsay (B). Portrait of Karl Marx, Chinese Chromo-litho, Private Collection (B). International Communist Magazine (B). The Bolshevik by Boris Kustodiev, Tretyakov Museum, Moscow (B). October: Also Sprach Zarathustra, Title Page (AKG). Nietzsche by E. Krauss (AKG). The Sea Serpent by G. Klimt, Österreichische Galerie, Vienna (B). Portrait of Sigmund Freud by Wilhelm Krausz, Private Collection (B). Judith by G. Klimt, Osterreichische Galerie, Vienna (B). November: Bertrand Russell by Kurt Hutton, Picture Post (HG). The Thinker by A. Rodin, Private Collection (B). Martin Heidegger by Gert Schuetz (AKG). The Wanderer over the Sea of Clouds by Caspar David Friedrich. December: Ludwig Wittgenstein (HG). Deckchair, Christine Jennings. The Backs by Albert Goodwin, V&A Museum, London (B). The Fitzwilliam Museum by JSM Harvey (B). Jean-Paul Sartre by Marc Riboud (Magnum).

B - Bridgeman, BL - British Library, BM - British Museum, HG - Hulton Getty, ME - Mary Evans Picture Library.

Alberto pointed down to a
particular book and Sophie
gasped as she read the title:

SOPHIE'S WORLD

*"Would yOu like me to
buy it for you?"*

"I don't know if I dare!"